First edition 2017

Copyright © 2017 Anno Domini Publishing
www.ad-publishing.com
Text copyright © 2017 Sally Ann Wright
Illustrations copyright © 2016, 2017 Frank Endersby

Published 2017 by Authentic Media Ltd
PO Box 6326, Bletchley, Milton Keynes, MK1 9GG, UK
Conforms to EN71 and AS/NZS ISO 8124

Publishing Director: Annette Reynolds
Art Director: Gerald Rogers
Pre-production Manager: Doug Hewitt

Printed and bound in China

A First Bible for Children

Sally Ann Wright
and Frank Endersby

Contents

God's beautiful world

God was there in the very
beginning. God made a beautiful
world and filled it with colourful
fish and birds. God made
elephants with wiggly trunks and
lions with golden manes. God
made spotted ladybirds and stripy
tigers. God also made people,
you and me, to be his friends
and to look after his wonderful
world.

Noah's ark

Noah was God's friend. He loved God and listened to him. But the other people in the world were unkind and selfish and they liked to hurt each other. God told Noah that a big flood would come and wash the world clean. Noah listened to God. Then he built a huge boat and filled it with all the animals. When the flood came, God kept Noah, his family and all the animals safe till the waters went down.

Abraham moves away

A long time after Noah lived,
Abraham listened to God. God told
Abraham that he would bless him
and make his family into a huge
nation. But first Abraham needed
to move to a new land, a beautiful
land with mountains and rivers

and plenty to eat and drink. Abraham
didn't know where he was going.
He didn't know what would happen
there. But Abraham trusted God and
he went. And God blessed him.

Jacob's favourite son

Joseph was Abraham's great-grandson. He was the favourite of his father, Jacob. But Jacob had a large family and because he loved Joseph

the best, Joseph's brothers didn't like him at all. When Joseph started wearing a beautiful coat that his father had given to him, his brothers decided Joseph must go!

Joseph,
the hero

Joseph's brothers told Jacob that Joseph had been killed by
a wild animal — but it was not true! The brothers had sold
him as a slave to some traders. For years Joseph worked

in Egypt but God took care of him. The great
king of Egypt noticed him and made him a very
important man. When Joseph's brothers came to
Egypt looking for food, Joseph helped them — and forgave
them for treating him so badly. 'Come here to Egypt to live.
God has brought us here to look after us.'

Slaves in Egypt

Jacob, his children, his grandchildren and his great-grandchildren came to live in Egypt. As time went on, Jacob died. Then Joseph died — and the king died. As new kings came and went, Abraham's huge family grew in Egypt. Then one day a new king saw how many of them there were. There were far too many! He called them the Hebrews. And he didn't like them. He made them all his slaves and worked them very hard.

A baby in a basket

The new king of Egypt saw that whatever he did, the
Hebrews grew stronger. So he told his soldiers to throw
all the baby boys into the big River Nile so that they could
not grow up to fight him. Miriam's mother was afraid

of the bad soldiers. She made a basket to hide her baby and put him by the big river. She knew God would keep him safe. Miriam watched as a princess found her little baby brother. She knew that nothing bad would happen to her little brother now.

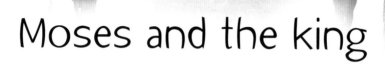

Moses and the king

Miriam's little brother was called Moses. He grew up in a palace but he never forgot who his family were. It made him very angry when he saw the Hebrews being treated badly by the Egyptians. Then one day God told him to go to the king and tell him, 'Let my people go!' Moses was afraid. He

couldn't do it! But he took his big brother Aaron and went to the king. 'I don't know your God,' said the king. 'I will not let his people go.'

Ten terrible plagues

Then some very bad things happened in the land of Egypt.
There were frogs and flies and horrible buzzing, stinging
things. The animals died, the people were very ill and all their

crops were destroyed. After each plague Moses
went to the king and gave him God's message,
'Let my people go!' Sometimes the king said yes,
but as soon as the plague had stopped, he changed his
mind. Finally, after the tenth plague, the king told Moses
to take God's people and everything they owned and
'GO!'

Crossing the Red Sea

Moses led the people, hundreds and thousands of them, with sheep and goats and donkeys until they arrived at the Red Sea. Then the king changed his mind again and sent his chariots

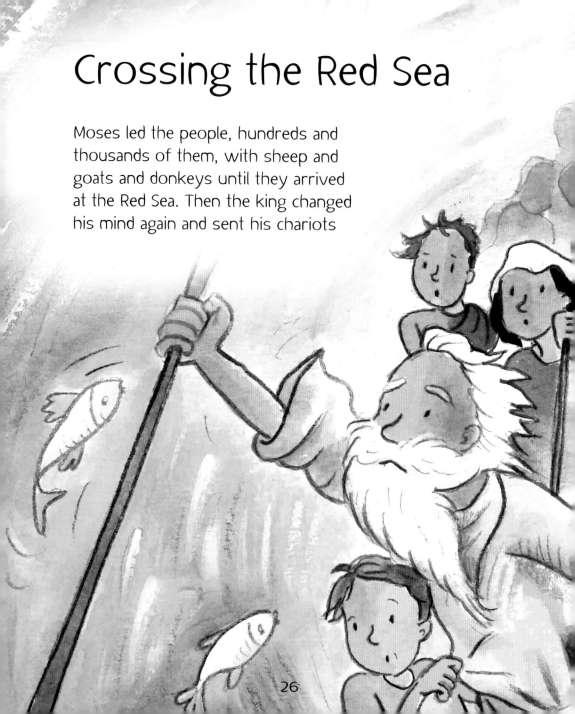

to chase after them! The sea was in front of them, the chariots were behind them... 'Trust God,' said Moses. And he held up his stick over the sea — and the waters parted to let the people cross to the other side.

Wandering in the desert

God's people were free. They were no longer slaves in Egypt. Moses led them through the desert to take them back to the land that he had given to Abraham where they could

be happy. When they were thirsty, God gave them water from a rock or led them to pools of clear water. When they were hungry, he gave them quails to eat and bread that tasted like honey.

Moses up the mountain

One day Moses climbed a mountain where God gave him rules, ten commandments that his people should keep. Then they would be happy. God told them to love him and him alone; they should respect his name and keep one special day to worship him. They should love and respect their parents. They must not murder or steal someone's wife or husband or steal anything at all from anyone. They should not tell lies to hurt someone else — and they should be happy with what they have, not always want what someone else has.

Spies in the land

When they reached the banks of the River Jordan, Moses sent twelve spies into the land to see if the people were friendly and whether the land was good to grow food. Joshua and Caleb came back to say that God had given them a beautiful country with lots of good things to eat. But the other ten men were afraid of the fierce people who lived there.

Joshua leads the people

Moses was a very old man. He died
before the people crossed into
the land God had promised them.
But God chose Joshua as the next
leader. 'Don't be afraid, Joshua,' said
God. 'Be strong and brave. I will
always be with you to help you.'

Rahab hides the spies

Before Joshua prepared the people to cross the River Jordan, he sent two men into the walled city of Jericho. They stayed with a woman called Rahab who hid them from the soldiers who

banged on her door. 'Everyone knows your God is the one who made heaven and earth,' she said. 'We know that he will help you take the city just as he led your people out of Egypt.'

The walls of Jericho

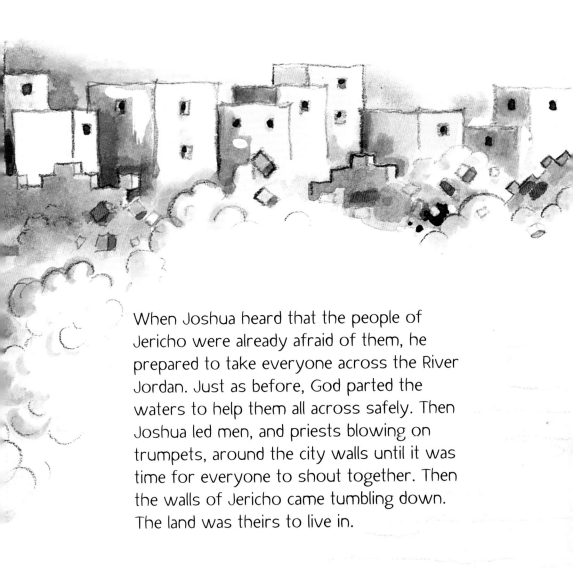

When Joshua heard that the people of Jericho were already afraid of them, he prepared to take everyone across the River Jordan. Just as before, God parted the waters to help them all across safely. Then Joshua led men, and priests blowing on trumpets, around the city walls until it was time for everyone to shout together. Then the walls of Jericho came tumbling down. The land was theirs to live in.

Hiding in a pit

A long time after Joshua, a man called Gideon was working in a pit so his enemies couldn't see him. Suddenly an angel appeared to him. 'God has chosen you, Gideon,' said the angel. 'He wants you to help his people.' Gideon didn't believe the angel. 'But I am no one!' he said. 'No one listens to me. I need a sign to be sure.'

A sign for Gideon

Gideon asked God to help him.
'Please make my fleece wet tonight
while the ground is dry,' he prayed.
When it happened just as he had

asked, Gideon prayed again. 'Please make my
fleece dry tonight while all the ground is wet.'
God answered his prayer. Then Gideon believed
that God would help him and was ready to do
what he asked.

God calls Samuel

Samuel was very young when he first went to work in the temple. He was a great help to Eli, the priest, and learned how to listen to God while he was there. One night, Samuel heard someone call his name. 'Here I am!' Samuel said, thinking that Eli had called him. But Eli sent him back to bed. 'I didn't call you,' he said. Again Samuel heard his name and went to Eli. When it happened a third time, Eli said, 'It is God who is calling you, Samuel. Listen to him and do everything he tells you.'

The first kings of Israel

Samuel helped the people
hear what God was saying
to them. He anointed Saul the
first king of Israel and when God saw that Saul
was not a good king, he helped Samuel find David. 'Go to
see Jesse,' said God. 'Meet his sons.' Samuel met seven of
Jesse's sons. They were all tall and strong and handsome.

But none of them were God's chosen king. 'You see what is on the outside,' said God. 'But I see what is in their hearts.' When Samuel met David, God told him that he was the right man to be king.

David and Goliath

King Saul and all his soldiers were afraid. They saw the huge giant called Goliath challenge them to come and fight him every day. 'I will fight him,' said David. He wouldn't wear the king's armour — it was too big. He wouldn't take his sword — it was too heavy. 'God has kept me safe from the lions and bears when I take care of my father's sheep. God will take care of me now.' And the giant fell down dead when David used his shepherd's sling against him.

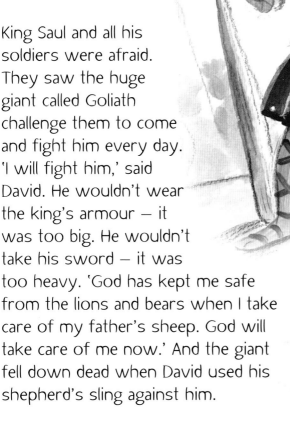

Ravens bring food

There was nothing to eat and nothing to drink. 'I will show you where to go, Elijah,' said God. God sent Elijah to a little bubbling stream. Elijah drank the clear water and wasn't thirsty any more. God sent ravens to bring Elijah food every day. Elijah ate the food and wasn't hungry any more. 'Thank you, God, for taking care of me,' said Elijah.

A little drop of oil

When the stream had dried up, God sent Elijah to a town where he met a kind woman. 'Will you share your bread with me?' Elijah asked. 'I have almost nothing left to eat,' she said. 'I will bake bread with my last drop of oil and the last of my flour — and then my son and I will die.' But the woman shared the bread with Elijah. And for as long as she shared, there was always another drop of oil and a little more flour left to bake some more bread.

God's gentle voice

The king hated Elijah and the king's wife wanted to kill him! Elijah was afraid. He felt very much alone. He went away by himself and hid in a cave. God told Elijah he would meet him on the mountain. Elijah heard a roaring wind around him; but

God was not in the wind. There was an earthquake and there was fire; but God was not there in the fire. When God came, he came with a gentle whisper; and he comforted Elijah.

Jonah runs away

Jonah didn't want to listen to God. He sailed away on a ship hoping God wouldn't find him. But God is bigger than the sea and he knew just where Jonah was. A huge storm tossed the boat up and down until the sailors threw Jonah over the

side. Then God sent a huge fish to save Jonah — and Jonah was sorry he hadn't listened. The fish left him on a beach — and Jonah did all that God asked him to do.

Daniel and the lions

Daniel loved God and talked to him every day. But the silly king made a law that people should pray only to him – or they would be thrown to the lions! Daniel still loved God and he still talked to God every day. But when Daniel was thrown to the lions, God was there to look after him. God closed the lions' mouths and saved him.

Mary's little baby

An angel told Mary that she would have a very special baby boy. He would be God's son and his name would be Jesus. Mary went with Joseph to Bethlehem and when her special baby was born, Mary

made a bed for him in the manger because there was no
room at the inn. Then shepherds came to worship him
because they knew Jesus was the saviour of the world.

Jesus, the baby king

A new star appeared in the sky when Jesus was born. Wise men from the East followed it, hoping to find a baby who was born to be the king of the Jewish people. They brought gifts for the special baby and when they found Jesus in a house in Bethlehem, they bowed down and worshipped him.

Jesus is baptised

When Jesus was a man he went to the River Jordan. John was there baptising people. 'I want you to baptise me,' said

Jesus. But John knew who Jesus was. 'I can't do that,' he said. 'You are the special one, sent by God. You should be baptising me!' But Jesus knew that God would be pleased. And when he came up from the water, everyone heard God's voice. 'This is my son. I love him,' said God.

Choosing special friends

Jesus lived by the Sea of Galilee. One day he asked Peter to take out his boat into deeper water where there were fish to catch. Peter and his brother Andrew had been fishing all night and caught nothing, but when they went with Jesus, their nets filled with so many fish they nearly broke! Then Jesus asked them and their friends, James and John, to

come with him and be his friends.
They were the first of twelve men
who became his disciples, travelling
with Jesus, listening to him, seeing
all the things he did and learning
from him.

The man who couldn't walk

Jesus told people that God loved them. He healed people who were blind or deaf or who couldn't walk. One day four men brought their friend to Jesus. They lowered him through the roof so that Jesus could help him. That day the man was able to walk home because Jesus had healed him.

Jesus calms a storm

Jesus sailed across the lake in his friends' fishing boat.
Jesus had been helping people all day and he was so tired,
he fell asleep. But thunder crashed and lightning flashed
and the boat tipped up and down. 'Help us!' his friends
shouted. They were very frightened. Jesus spoke to the
wind and the waves and the storm died down and all was
quiet again.

A huge picnic lunch

People followed Jesus
everywhere. They wanted to
hear him talk about God. But
one day Jesus saw that the
people were hungry. He wanted
to give them something to eat.
A boy brought him some bread
and fish — his own picnic lunch.
And Jesus thanked God and
shared out all the food — and
over 5,000 people had enough
to eat!

The secret of happiness

'God blesses people who are not too proud to ask for his help,' said Jesus. 'God comforts people who are sad and will be kind to people who are kind to others. Love people and treat them kindly — even if they are not kind to you. Forgive them if they hurt you. Treat them as you would like to be treated yourself,' said Jesus. 'Love your enemies and pray for them. That's the secret of happiness.'

How should I pray?

When people asked Jesus how they should pray, Jesus told them to talk to God knowing he was their loving Father in heaven. 'You don't need to use long words. God knows what you need. Tell him what you feel and ask him to help you. God is kind and generous. Be honest with him and he will bless you and give you all you need.'

The little
lost sheep

Jesus was good at telling stories. 'Imagine
you are a shepherd with 100 sheep. One
day you find that one little sheep is lost.

What do you do? You look everywhere until you carry that lost sheep home on your shoulders because every one of your sheep is special to you. God loves you just as that good shepherd loves his sheep.'

The Good Samaritan

One of Jesus' stories was about being kind to anyone who needs our help — even people we don't know. The man in the story was called the Good Samaritan. He helped a man who had been robbed and was hurt — even when other 'good' people didn't stop to help him. 'Be like the Good Samaritan,' said Jesus. 'That's how God wants you to live.'

Treasure in heaven

'Once a rich farmer had such a good harvest that he built bigger barns to store all his crops,' said Jesus. 'He planned to enjoy all the good things he had stored up. But that night,

the man died. His riches were no good to him any more.
So don't be greedy. Life is more important than the things
money can buy. Share what you have with people who need
it and store up treasure in heaven where moths cannot eat it
and robbers cannot break in and steal it.'

'Let the children come to me'

Jesus had time for everyone — mums and dads, grandmas and grandpas, people who had no one to love them or look after them — and especially children. When his friends said that Jesus was busy, Jesus welcomed them. Jesus told

them that we are all special to God. God is happy when we tell him about everything that worries us. God cares about us and loves us very much.

A very little man

Zacchaeus was a very little man.
No one liked him. They called
him a cheat. Zacchaeus wanted
very much to meet Jesus. But
he couldn't see Jesus because of
the crowd. So Zacchaeus climbed

a tree. Now he could see Jesus — and Jesus was happy to meet him! 'I won't be a cheat any more,' he told Jesus. 'I will pay back all I took and more — and I will share everything I have with the poor.' Jesus was pleased. 'I came to help people like Zacchaeus,' he said.

The blind man who begged

Bartimaeus could not see. So Bartimaeus sat
by the city wall and asked people for money
so that he could eat. When he heard that
Jesus was coming, he was very excited.
Perhaps Jesus would help him. And Jesus

did! Jesus healed his eyes so
Bartimaeus could see. And
then he followed Jesus
everywhere, telling
everyone what Jesus
had done for him.

Riding on a donkey

Jesus rode into Jerusalem on a donkey. Many people loved Jesus and they waved and cheered. They spread palm leaves on the ground in front of him. 'Hooray for Jesus, our king!' they shouted. But not everyone was happy. Some jealous men began to plot against him. And Judas decided to help them. They gave Judas money to tell them where they could find Jesus alone.

The Servant King

Jesus met with his
friends to have supper.
First he washed their
dusty feet. 'But this is a

servant's job!' said Peter. 'You shouldn't do
this!' But Jesus carried on. 'I am doing this
to show you that you must take care of
one another. No one is too important to do
this. This is how we show that we love one
another.'

The last supper

'This is the last time we will eat supper together,'
said Jesus. 'Soon I will be taken away from you.
I will go to prepare a place for you in heaven.
Everyone is welcome there but first I must go to
make it ready.' Jesus shared some bread with them.
Then he shared a cup of wine 'Eat this bread — it
is my body. Drink this wine — it is my blood.' But
where was Judas? He had gone out into the night.

Praying in the garden

They went together to a garden
of olive trees. Jesus prayed
that God would help him to be
brave. He knew that some very

bad things were going to happen. Then Judas, one
of his friends, came through the darkness with
torches — and brought men with swords and
clubs. They arrested Jesus and marched him off.
His friends were so afraid that they ran away.

97

Jesus dies on a cross

His friends could not believe the terrible things that happened next. Their dear friend, Jesus, was beaten and made to carry a cross to a hill outside the town. There he died between two thieves. His friends took his body down from the cross and buried him in a tomb. A heavy stone door was pushed in front of the entrance.

Jesus is alive!

Mary Magdalene and some of the other
women went to the place where they had
seen Jesus buried. But the heavy stone door
had been moved — and the tomb was empty.
Then Mary met Jesus in the garden. He was
alive! 'Go and tell everyone that you have
seen me,' Jesus said.

The locked door

Soon Jesus went to see his
other friends. Nearly all of
them were together. The door

of the room was locked as they were all afraid after what had happened to Jesus. But suddenly Jesus was there in the room with them! They had something to eat. They talked together. They were very happy that he was alive and with them again.

Thomas needs to see Jesus

Thomas was not there when Jesus came. 'I can't believe it,' he told his friends. 'We know he died. You must be mistaken. Unless I see Jesus for myself — and see the wounds in his body — I won't believe Jesus is alive.' But Jesus came again. Thomas was amazed. He saw Jesus for himself — and he saw that he was alive!

Breakfast on the beach

One morning Jesus helped his friends find a huge catch
of fish. Then they sat and ate breakfast with him on
the beach. Jesus promised to give them his Holy Spirit
to help them live the way God wanted them to. All his
friends now knew that Jesus was alive and he would
never die again. He would go back to God in heaven and
make a home for them there.

Jesus returns to heaven

For forty days Jesus came and went. He appeared to small groups and sometimes larger crowds. All his followers knew that they had seen Jesus and talked with him. He was alive. Jesus told them to tell people everywhere what had happened and to share with them all that he had taught them. Then Jesus seemed to disappear into a cloud. He had returned to his Father in heaven.

The Holy Spirit comes

Jesus' friends were in Jerusalem when the Holy Spirit
came to them. They heard a sound like the wind. They saw
what looked like flames of fire. But instead of being afraid,

suddenly they knew that they could do anything God wanted them to do. They knew that he was there to help them serve God and give them the power they needed to help other people.

The beggar by the gate

When Peter and John went to pray in the
Temple, they were met at the gate by a man
who couldn't walk. Day after day he sat and
begged for coins. 'I don't have any money I can
give you, but Jesus has given me the power to
give you something much better. Stand up and
walk!' Then the man found that he could stand
up! He ran about telling everyone how great
God was for making him well again!

The man in the chariot

Philip found himself on the road to Gaza where he met a man in a chariot trying to understand something he was reading. The Holy Spirit helped Philip to explain that Jesus had died in his place on the cross, and the man asked Philip to baptise him in a nearby stream. The man returned to his own country to share what he knew about Jesus with others he met.

Paul meets Jesus

Paul was on a journey to Damascus.
He thought the Christians were
wrong and wanted to find them and
put them in prison. Suddenly there

was a blinding light all around him. He fell to his knees and heard a voice call his name. 'I have a job for you to do,' said Jesus. 'Go into the city and someone will come and tell you what it is.' Paul was amazed: he had heard Jesus speaking to him — the man he had thought was dead. From that day Paul was a changed man.

God speaks to Peter

All Jesus' friends were Jewish. They believed that only Jewish people could know God and be his special people. But God spoke to Peter in a vision where he was told to eat animals that had always been forbidden to Jewish people. God showed him that Jesus had opened the way for anyone and everyone to know God and be a friend of Jesus. They could be male or

female, old or young and come
from any place on earth. God
wanted everyone to know him
and to be his friends, just like in
the very beginning.

God answers prayer

Soon many people were Christians. But they were not safe. Peter was chained up in prison between two soldiers. His friends prayed together that God would keep him safe. That night an angel appeared in the prison cell. The chains fell off Peter's wrists, doors opened and closed by a miracle and he followed the angel out of the prison. Peter's friends were amazed and overjoyed to see him safe. God had answered their prayers.

The sinking ship

Paul travelled to many places to tell people about Jesus. But he was also put in prison many times. While he was a prisoner on a ship sailing to Rome, his ship was wrecked in a storm off the coast of Malta. Some swam to the beach; others clung to the wreckage, but everyone on board reached the shore safely. God had kept them all

safe. When Paul reached Rome, he stayed in a house, with a soldier to guard him, sharing what he knew about Jesus.

The message of love

Paul wrote letters to Christians
everywhere to help them live the way
God wanted them to. He taught them
that they could show people how
much they loved God by loving others.
'Love is patient and kind. Love is not
greedy or proud or rude. Love always
thinks of other people first. Love
doesn't get angry or remind people of
the bad things they've done. Love lasts
for ever.' Now there are followers of
Jesus all over the world.